D1095411

Edition Eulenburg

Meister Richard Wagner
in tiefster Ehrfurcht gewidmet

SYMPHONY No. 3

D minor

by

ANTON BRUCKNER

First performed Dec. 16th 1877 in Vienna,

Gesellschaft der Musikfreunde, Bruckner conducting

Foreword by Hans F. Redlich

RICHMOND PUBLIC LIBRARY CALIFORNIA

Ernst Eulenburg, Ltd. London, W.1.
Edition Eulenburg, G,m.b.H., Zurich
Edition Eulenburg, Inc. New York

M
785.11

Anton Bruckner—Symphony No. 3 in D Minor

Bruckner's third Symphony holds a unique place in his symphonic oeuvre:— It was singled out by Richard Wagner himself to be dedicated to him; work on it occupied Bruckner off and on for nearly 18 years, and, finally, it was published in two different versions during the composer's lifetime. The extended struggle for perfection resulted in the case of the "Wagner" Symphony in a number of versions which epitomise Bruckner's development as a symphonist from the early days of his "Mass" Symphonies down to the final period of Symphonies 8 and 9. There are four different drafts extant of the autograph of the full score. They eventually crystallised into two published versions of the full score. These two published versions are not only at variance with themselves, but also differ widely from the autograph versions which led up to them. Hence, the history of this work and its ever changing appearance can best be presented in the following tabulated form:—

Version 1, composed 1872/73; full score completed 31st December 1873; unpublished.

It is this early draft which was presented to Wagner in Bayreuth in September 1873 in an incomplete form, for the Finale had not been orchestrated by that date.

Version 2, composed 1874, represents an improvement on Version 1; unpublished.

This was sent to Wagner in a fair copy in Spring 1874.

Version 3, composed 1876/78.

This third version became the basis for the first publication of the full score which, however, differs in a number of cases from the autograph. That first publication appeared in 1878. It was reprinted in 1950 in an edition for which Fritz Oeser was

Bruckners 3. Symphonie nimmt einen besonderen Platz in seinen symphonischen Werken ein: sie wurde von Richard Wagner selbst ausgesucht, um ihm gewidmet zu werden. Die Arbeit daran beschäftigte Bruckner mit Unterbrechungen nahezu 18 Jahre, und schliesslich wurde sie bei seinen Lebzeiten in zwei verschiedenen Fassungen gedruckt. Bruckners andauernder Kampf um Vollkommenheit führte bei der "Wagner"-Symphonie zu einer Anzahl von Fassungen, die bezeichnend sind für seine Entwickelung als Symphoniker von den frühen Zeiten seiner "Messe"-Symphonien bis zu der letzten Periode von No. 8 und 9. Es gibt 4 verschiedene Entwürfe des Autographs der Partitur, deren Ergebnis die zwei veröffentlichten Fassungen waren. Diese zwei Fassungen unterscheiden sich nicht nur von einander, sondern auch stark von den autographen Fassungen, die zu ihnen geführt haben. Die Geschichte dieses Werkes und seine wechselnde Erscheinungsform kann somit folgendermassen registriert werden:

Fassung 1, komponiert 1872/3; Partitur beendet 31. Dezember 1873; nicht veröffentlicht. Dieser frühe Entwurf wurde im September 1873 Wagner in unvollständiger Form vorgelegt; denn das Finale war damals noch nicht instrumentiert.

Fassung 2, komponiert 1874, eine Verbesserung von Fassung 1; nicht veröffentlicht.

Sie wurde Wagner in einer Reinschrift im Frühling 1874 geschickt.

Fassung 3, komponiert 1876–78, wurde die Basis für die erste Veröffentlichung der Partitur, weicht aber in einer Zahl von Einzelheiten vom Autograph ab. Diese erste Ausgabe erschien 1878 und wurde 1950 neu gedruckt, herausgegeben von Fritz

C.1

responsible. The original title page runs as follows:—

Oeser. Die Original-Titelseite lautet:

Symphonie
in
(D Moll)
für grosses Orchester
componirt
von
Anton Bruckner
Verlag von A. Bösendorfer's
Musikalienhandlung
(Bussjäger & Rättig)
Wien.

The dedication page reads:—

Die Widmungsseite lautet:

Meister
Richard Wagner
in tiefster Verehrung gewidmet.

The first performance of the first print of the Symphony took place on 16th December, 1877, under Bruckner's direction. The performance, which should have been conducted by Johann Herbeck but for his untimely death on October 28th, 1877, was a complete failure but resulted in the subsequent publication of the full score and in the simultaneous publication of an arrangement for piano duet, undertaken by Gustav Mahler and Rudolf Krzyzanowski. The debacle of 1877 and the little interest aroused by the publication of 1878 prompted Brucker finally—in a period of great depression caused by Hermann Levi's refusal to accept Symphony No. 8 for performance in 1887—to revise the work for the fourth time.

Version 4, based on the published score of 1878, extended over the years 1888/89. It suffered an interruption through a visit of Mahler who thought that the revision was unnecessary. In the end Bruckner was persuaded by the brothers Joseph and Franz Schalk to complete that version, which in turn became the basis for the second published score of 1890. Its title page runs as follows:—

Die Erstaufführung dieses ersten Druckes fand am 16. Dezember 1877 unter Bruckners Leitung statt. Sie sollte von Johann Herbeck dirigiert werden, der aber am 28. Oktober gestorben war. Sie war ein völliger Misserfolg, gab aber den Anlass zur Herausgabe der Partitur und gleichzeitig einer Bearbeitung für Klavier 4-händig durch Gustav Mahler und Rudolf Krzyzanowski. Diese Schlappe und das das geringe Interesse, das die Veröffentlichung von 1878 fand, veranlasste Bruckner schliesslich—zur Zeit einer tiefen Depression infolge von Hermann Levis Ablehnung seiner 8. Symphonie für eine Aufführung im Jahre 1887—das Werk zum 4. Male zu revidieren.

Fassung 4 beruht auf der erschienenen Partitur von 1878, ausgearbeitet 1888/9. Die Arbeit wurde unterbrochen durch einen Besuch von Mahler, der die Revision für unnötig hielt. Schliesslich wurde Bruckner durch die Brüder Joseph und Franz Schalk überredet, die Fassung doch durchzuführen; und sie wurde nun die Basis für die 2. gedruckte Partitur von 1890. Die Titelseite lautet:

Symphonie
D Moll
für grosses Orchester
componirt von
Anton Bruckner
Verlag von Theodor Rättig in Wien.

Only on page 5, i.e. page 1 of the first Movement, the heading "Dritte Symphonie" is to be found. The first performance of this second printed version took place on December 21st, 1890, in a concert of the Vienna Philharmonic Orchestra conducted by Hans Richter. It was a tremendous success and Bruckner took 12 calls. The same Philharmonic Orchestra had three times refused to play the Symphony during 1875-77! Again, as in 1878, the published score of 1890 differs from the autograph of Version 4. This has become quite clear when that "Stichvorlage" was published as Volume 3/3 of the complete critical edition of Bruckner's works, edited by Leopold Nowak, Vienna, 1959.

As long as not every one of these six different versions is accessible in print, the respective merits of each of them cannot be properly assessed. It is not impossible that only a seventh final version, which will unite the achievements and characteristics of each of its predecessors may become the universally accepted performing edition of the future. The reasons for Bruckner's extraordinary preoccupation with this particular work are not far to seek. It is the first of his Symphonies to create the archetype of a "Bruckner" Symphony with its derivation from Beethoven's 9th Symphony, its interplanetary thematic links with Bruckner's Masses and, last but not least, its associations with Wagner's music. As for the latter, the unpublished version (1) abounded in deliberate quotations from Wagner's "Walküre", "Tristan" and "Meistersinger". They were all but expunged from the later versions. The thematic allusions to Bruckner's Mass

Erst auf p.5, d.h. p.1 des 1. Satzes, ist die Überschrift "Dritte Symphonie" zu finden. Die Erstaufführung dieser 2. gedruckten Fassung fand am 21. Dezember 1890 in einem Konzert des Wiener Philharmonischen Orchesters unter Hans Richter statt. Es war ein enormer Erfolg, und Bruckner wurde 12mal gerufen. Dasselbe Orchester hatte vorher 3mal das Werk abgelehnt. Wiederum, wie schon 1878, wich die gedruckte Partitur vom Autographen der Fassung 4 ab. Das wurde klar, als die "Stichvorlage" als Band 3/3 der vollständigen, kritischen Ausgabe von Bruckners Werken von Leopold Nowak 1959 veröffentlicht wurde.

Solange nicht jede dieser 6 Fassungen im Druck vorliegt, ist es unmöglich, ihren Wert abzuschätzen. Es ist nicht ausgeschlossen, dass erst eine 7. endgiltige Fassung die Ergebnisse und Charakterzüge aller ihrer Vorgängerinnen vereinigen und die allgemein anerkannte Aufführungsform der Zukunft bilden wird. Die Gründe für Bruckners aussergewöhnliche Skrupel bei diesem Werk sind nicht schwer zu finden. Es ist die erste seiner Symphonien, die den Prototyp einer "Bruckner"-Symphonie schuf, mit seiner Ableitung von Beethovens 9. Symphonie, seinen weitgeschwungenen thematischen Bindungen mit Bruckners Messen, und nicht zuletzt mit Wagners Musik. Was die letztere betrifft, so ist die unveröffentlichte Fassung 1 reich an absichtlichen Zitaten aus Wagners "Walküre", "Tristan" und "Meistersinger". Sie wurden fast durchweg in den späteren Fassungen ausgemerzt. Aber die thematischen Anspielungen auf Bruckners D moll-Messe (1864), deren

in D Minor (1864), whose "Miserere" section is re-echoed in the first Movement of the published score No. 2 (1890), bars 217–238, however, remained untouched in the course of the many metamorphoses of this work. The most striking difference between the two published scores of 1878 and 1890 is an intrinsic change in the climate of orchestration. In the score of 1890 the tendency towards the magniloquent orchestral style of Symphonies 7 and 8 becomes noticeable. While it is quite possible to lay much of the added expression-marks, bowings, slurs and doublings at the door of the brothers Schalk, it is impossible to overlook the changed orchestral atmosphere of certain sections which Bruckner himself re-composed expressly for this second publication. A case in point, amply discussed in Fritz Oeser's meritorious preface of 1950, is the passage at the end of the development section of Movement 1 (bars 373–401), score of 1890. The publication of 1890 was undertaken by Bruckner himself, albeit with the help of his disciples, and he alone must bear full responsibility for it. Hence, it is not only permissible but quite legitimate to perform the published score of 1890 even if it compares badly with some sections of the published score of 1878.

Symphony No. 3, in its second printed version of 1890, bears the hallmark of creative importance by virtue of its principal thematic subjects as well as by the choice of its principal key of D Minor. The latter links it not only with works like the Mass in D Minor and the "Zero" Symphony of 1863/64, but also with Bruckner's loftiest conception:— the unfinished Symphony No. 9 in D Minor. The sign-manual of the whole work is the interval of the bare Fifth, so well known from the Introduction of Beethoven's 9th Symphony and from the Overture to Wagner's "Flying Dutchman". That interval becomes, as

"Miserere"-Abschnitt im 1. Satz der gedruckten Partitur No. 2, Takte 217–238, wiederklingt, blieb im Laufe der vielen Metamorphosen dieses Werkes unberührt. Der auffallendste Gegensatz zwischen den 2 gedruckten Partituren von 1878 und 1890 ist der grundsätzliche Wechsel in der Art der Instrumentation. in der Ausgabe von 1890 ist die Neigung zu dem monumentalen Orchesterstil der Symphonien No. 7 und 8 deutlich erkennbar. Während vielleicht ein guter Teil der hinzugefügten Vortragszeichen, Stricharten, Bögen und Verdoppelungen den Brüdern Schalk zugeschoben werden kann, lässt sich die veränderte orchestrale Färbung gewisser Partien unmöglich übersehen, die Bruckner selbst ausdrücklich für die 2. Ausgabe neu komponiert hat. Ein Beispiel hierfür, das in Fritz Oesers verdienstvollen Vorwort von 1950 erörtert wird, ist die Stelle am Ende des Durchführungsteiles des 1. Satzes (Takte 373–401) der Fassung von 1890. Diese Ausgabe wurde von Bruckner selbst veranstaltet, wenn auch mit der Hilfe seiner Schüler, und er allein ist verantwortlich dafür. Deshalb ist es nicht nur zulässig, sondern durchaus gerechtfertigt, die gedruckte Fassung von 1890 aufzuführen, selbst wenn einige Stellen hinter der Fassung von 1878 zurückstehen.

Symphonie No. 3, in der 2. gedruckten Fassung von 1890 trägt das Kennzeichen schöpferischer Bedeutung durch ihre wichtigsten Themen sowie durch die Haupttonart D moll. Letztere verbindet sie nicht nur mit Werken wie der Messe in D moll und der "nullten" Symphonie von 1863/4, sondern auch mit Bruckners grossartigster Konzeption, der unvollendeten Symphonie No. 9. Das Symbol des ganzen Werkes ist das Intervall der leeren Quinte, der aus der Introduktion zu Beethovens 9. Symphonie und aus Wagners Holländer-Ouvertüre so wohl bekannt ist. Dieses Intervall beherrscht die ganze Symphonie. Sein hohler

it were, the integral of the whole Symphony. Its hollow scream pervades the thematic expositions of Movements 1, 3 and 4. But it also determines the intervallic structure of the famous trumpet-theme which aroused Wagner's admiration, and which dominates not only the first Movement but also the Coda of the Finale:—

Klang durchdringt die thematischen Expositionen des 1., 3. und 4. Satzes. Aber er bestimmt auch die Struktur des berühmten Trompeten - Themas, das Wagners Bewunderung erregte, und das nicht nur den 1. Satz, sondern auch die Coda des Finale beherrscht:

Music Example 1

In addition it is contained by implication in the background-motif to Example 1 which was bodily lifted out of the exposition of the "Zero" Symphony:—

Ausserdem ist er folgerichtig enthalten in der Hintergrundsmusik zu Beispiel 1, die genau der Exposition der "Nullten" Symphonie entnommen ist:

Music Example 2

The connection with Beethoven's 9th Symphony rests not only on the interval of the bare Fifth. The very process of a thematic stretto underpinned by a chromatic 4-note ostinato

Der Zusammenhang mit Beethovens 9. Symphonie ist nicht auf das Intervall der leeren Quinte beschränkt. Gerade der Prozess des thematischen Stretto, untermalt durch ein 4-Noten-Ostinato

Music Example 3

is modelled on the Coda to the first Movement of Beethoven's Symphony. Bruckner's favourite quintuplet rhythm

ist nach der Coda zum 1. Satz von Beethovens Symphonie entworfen. Der von Bruckner bevorzugte Quintolen-Rhythmus

makes its first striking appearance in the lovely "Gesangsperiode" of the first Movement:—

erscheint zum 1. Male auffallend in der lieblichen Gesangsperiode des 1. Satzes:

Music Example 4

The association with the D Minor Mass, already mentioned, leads to a passage, close to the end of the exposition (bars 248-255), which sounds like an echo of Palestrina's "Stabat Mater".

The slow Movement in the key of E Flat Major forms a poignant contrast to the majestic starkness of the end of the first Movement with its reiterations of the trumpet motif. It is a humble prayer and its thematic material undoubtedly stems from the devotional music of the Roman Church of the 18th century. Its "Marienkadenz"

Die bereits erwähnte Ideenverbindung mit der Messe in D moll führt zu einer Stelle, dicht vor dem Ende der Exposition (Takte 248–255), die wie ein Echo von Palestrinas "Stabat Mater" klingt.

Der langsame Satz in Es dur bildet einen scharfen Gegensatz zu der majestätischen Strenge des Schlusses des 1. Satzes mit seinen Wiederholungen des Trompeten-Motivs. Er ist ein demütiges Gebet, und sein thematisches Material stammt zweifellos von der andachtsvollen Musik der katholischen Kirche aus dem 18. Jahrhundert. Seine "Marienkadenz"

Music Example 5

a favourite turn of Bruckner's church music and a motif cropping up again and again in the Masses of Haydn and Mozart, is especially evocative of that period, while the beautfiul mysterioso section, bars 73 ff, sounds like the dream-like echo of some ancient Marian hymn.

The Scherzo seems determined as much by the element of the bare Fifth as by Upper Austrian "Ländler" rhythms which culminate in the delicious Trio section with its saucy dialogue between violin and viola.

The Finale is closely linked to the first Movement not only by the return of the trumpet motif in the use of the interval of the "hollow Fifth", first intoned by the flutes, but also by Bruckner's predilection for a "motoric" motif which permeates the whole structure of the Symphony.

Music Example 6

In addition, the Movement's "Gesangsperiode" epitomises the stark contrasts of gaiety and death by the combination of a polka and a chorale, spelt bitonally by Bruckner himself:—

Music Example 7

It is in this Finale, as in the latter portions of the first Movement, that Bruckner was persuaded to the most extensive changes in musical texture as well as in orchestration.

The present reprint of Eulenburg's Miniature Score No. 461 is based on the printed score of 1890, but the musical text has been carefully revised and numerous printers' errors of the publication of 1890 as well as of the Eulenburg Miniature Score of 1937 have been corrected. The publication of the "Stichvorlage" to the score of 1890 (mentioned earlier in this Preface) enables students to separate Bruckner's own conception from those additions and emendations which are now attributed by common consent to the brothers Schalk. However, not all of them should be rejected out of hand only because they were suggested by the disciples to the master. In fact, they contain many felicities such as the beautiful and logical crescendo in oboes and horn at bar 100 of Movement 1, which alone enables a smooth passage from the bridge passage of the woodwinds to the first bar of the "Gesangsperiode". It is that passage which in the first Version of the Symphony ran thus:—

Die vorliegende Ausgabe der Symphonie beruht auf der gedruckten Partitur von 1890; aber der Notentext ist genau durchgesehen worden, und zahlreiche Druckfehler sowohl in dem Druck von 1890 als in der früheren Eulenburg-Ausgabe wurden verbessert. Die Veröffentlichung der Stichvorlage der Ausgabe von 1890 (oben erwähnt) ermöglicht es der Forschung, Bruckners eigene Ideen von den Zutaten und Verbesserungen zu trennen, die allgemein den Brüdern Schalk zugeschrieben werden. Indessen sollten diese nicht einfach deshalb verworfen werden, weil sie von den Schülern dem Meister vorgeschlagen wurden. In der Tat enthalten sie viel Gutes, wie z.B. das schöne und logische Crescendo in Oboen und Hörnern bei Takt 100 im 1. Satz, das allein einen glatten Übergang von der Überbrückung der Holzbläser zum 1. Takt der Gesangsperiode ermöglicht. Dieser Übergang lautete in der 1. Fassung der Symphonie so:

Music Example 8

and which Bruckner did not improve by his own final version:

Bruckner hat das durch seine eigene, endgiltige Fassung nicht verbessert:

Music Example 9

H. F. REDLICH,
University of Edinburgh,
Faculty of Music.

March, 1961.

BIBLIOGRAPHY

Robert Haas, "Bruckner", Potsdam 1934.
H. F. Redlich, "Bruckner and Mahler", London 1955.
Bruckner, 3. Symphonie in D Moll, 2. Fassung von 1878, mit Einführung von Fritz Oeser, Wiesbaden 1950.
Anton Bruckner, Sämtliche Werke, Band 3/3, 3. Symphonie in D Moll, Fassung von 1889, vorgelegt von Leopold Nowak, Wien 1959.

Symphonie No 3

I

Mäßig bewegt M.M. ♩=66

Anton Bruckner
1824 - 1896

No 461   E.E. 4553   Ernst Eulenburg Ltd.
London - Zurich

zu 2
20
Fl.
p poco a
Hb.
p
Kl.
p
poco a
Fg.
(F)
Hr.
(B)
poco a poco
II. III.
Tr.
(D)
poco a poco
Pk.
tr
pp
poco a poco
Vl.
poco a poco
poco a
Br.
poco a
Vc.
tr
poco a poco
Kb.
poco a poco

8

E. E. 4553

13

E. E. 4553

Ursprüngliches Tempo

110

19

160
zu 2
Fl.
Hb.
Kl.
Fg.
(F)
Hr.
(B)
Tr.
(D)
Pos.
Vl.
Br.
Vc.
Kb.
fff marc.
pp
p
poco a poco cresc.
I.
III.
get.

24

E. E. 4553

30

E. E. 4553

34

E. E. 4553

35

E. E. 4553

36

E. E. 4553

38

E. E. 4553

E. E. 4553

44

E. H. 4553

49

E. E. 4553

E. E. 4553

54

E. E. 4553

58

60

66

69

E. E. 4553

70

E. E. 4553

72

Etwas langsamer

E. E. 4553

590
Tempo I
Tr.
(D)
Pk.
tr
pp
Vl.
Br.
6
Vc.
Kb.
600
Fl.
Hb.
Kl.
zu 2
Fg.
(F)
Hr.
(B)
IV.
I.
III.
II.
Pos.
poco a poco

E. E. 4553

620

Langsamer

zu 2
640
Fl.
Hb.
zu 2
Kl.
Fg.
(F)
Hr.
(B)
zu 2
I. II. zu 2
Tr.
(D)
I.
Pos.
II. III. zu 2
Pk.
Vl.
Br.
Vc.
Kb.

81

E. E. 4553

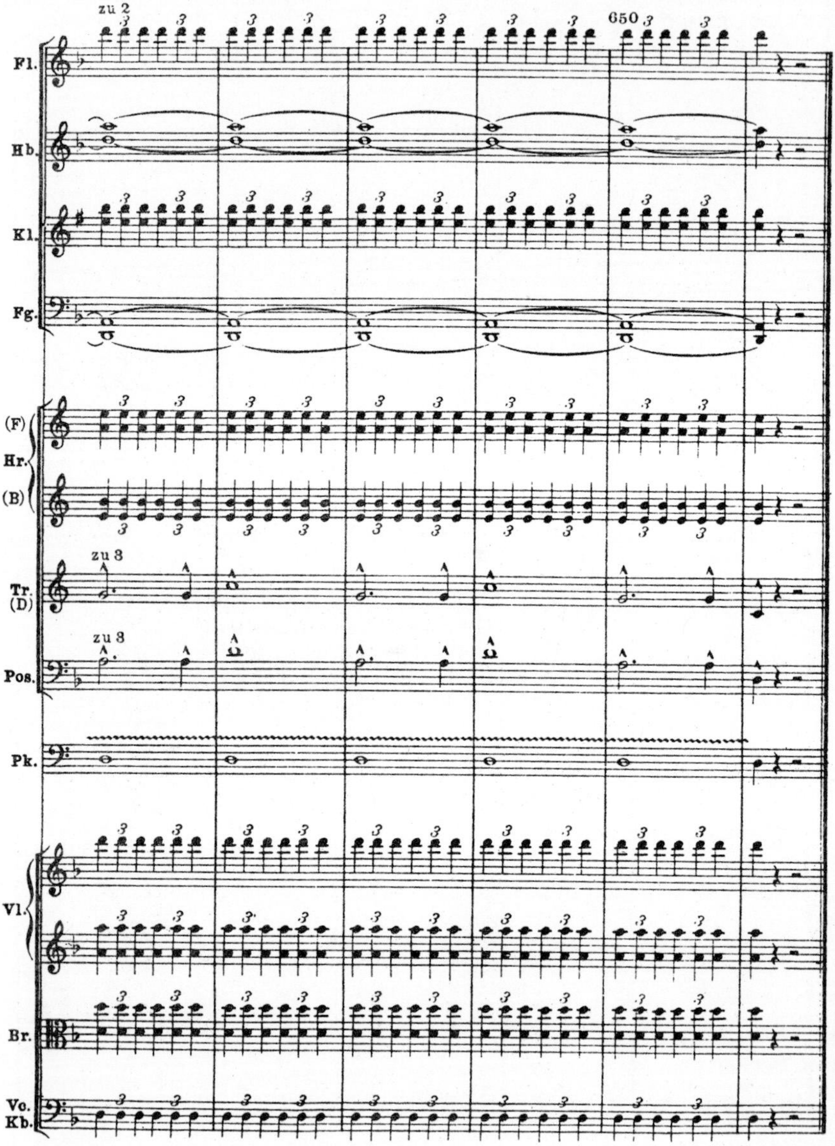
zu 2
650
Fl.
Hb.
Kl.
Fg.
(F)
Hr.
(B)
zu 3
Tr.
(D)
zu 3
Pos.
Pk.
Vl.
Br.
Vc.
Kb.

II

85

E. E. 4553

40
Fl.
Hb.
Kl.
Fg.
(F) Hr. (B)
Vl.
Br.
Vc.
Kb.
Andante (quasi Allegretto)
get.
hervortretend
50
riten.
sempre
cresc.
dim.

89

70 rit.

Misterioso (Langsamer)

80

E. E. 4553

Andante quasi Allegretto

96

E. E. 4553

103

E. E. 4553

104

E. E. 4553

III Scherzo

111

E. E. 4553

zu 2
30
Fl.
ff sempre
zu 2
Hb.
ff
zu 2
Kl.
ff
Fg.
ff
sf
sf
(F)
Hr.
(B)
ff
zu 2
ff
zu 3
Tr.
(D)
Pos.
sf
sf
trem.
Pk.
ff
Vl.
ff
ff
Br.
ff
Vc.
Kb.
ff
sf
sf

115

E. E. 4553

E. E. 4553

124

E. E. 4553

126

E. E. 4553

128

E. E. 4553

E.E.4553

132

E. E. 4553

270

Scherzo D.C.

IV Finale

138

E. E. 4553

E. E. 4553

144

145

E. E. 4553

130
I. allein
(F)
Hr.
(Es)
in Des
Tr.
(Des)
espress.
Pos.
Vl.
Br.
Vo.
Kb.
poco f
II.
Fl.
Hb.
Kl.
Fg.
I.
Hr.
(F)
p hervortretend
zu 2
cresc. sempre
cresc.

155

E. E. 4553

158

162

E. E. 4553

174

E. E. 4553

E. E. 4553

E. E. 4553

183

E. E. 4553

E. E. 4553

E. E. 4553

192

E. E. 4553

E. E. 4553

198

E. E. 4553

199

E. E. 4553

zu 2
480
Fl.
ff
Hb.
ff
Kl.
zu 2
ff
Fg.
ff
(F)
Hr.
(F)
ff
ff
Tr.
(D)
I.
II.
III.
ff
I.II. zu 2
III.
Pos.
I.
II.
III. ff
ff
Pk.
tr
Vl.
fff
fff
Br.
fff
Vo.
fff
Kb.
fff

202

FB 25217